The Old Fashioned Rules of Punctuation Book

The no-nonsense, proudly old-fashioned rules of punctuation to learn and remember for life

Ward Lock Educational Co. Ltd

WARD LOCK EDUCATIONAL CO. LTD.
1 CHRISTOPHER ROAD
EAST GRINSTEAD
SUSSEX RH19 3BT
UNITED KINGDOM

A MEMBER OF THE LING KEE GROUP
HONG KONG · SINGAPORE · LONDON · NEW YORK

Text © Dodi Beardshaw

First published – 1982
Reprinted – 1992 (twice), 1993

ISBN 0-7062-4123-1

Other titles in this series:
The Old Fashioned Rules of Grammar Book
ISBN 0 7062 3850 8
The Old Fashioned Rules of Spelling Book
ISBN 0 7062 4085 5
The Old Fashioned Handwriting Book
ISBN 0 7062 4139 8
The Old Fashioned Multiplication Book
ISBN 0 7062 4121 5
The Old Fashioned Division Book
ISBN 0 7062 4122 3
The Old Fashioned Adding-Up Book
ISBN 0 7062 4086 3
The Old Fashioned Taking-Away Book
ISBN 0 7062 4148 7
The Old Fashioned Mental Arithmetic Book
ISBN 0 7062 4160 6
The Old Fashioned Times Table Book
ISBN 0 7062 3749 8

Printed in Hong Kong

The old fashioned rules of punctuation

Start sentences with a *capital letter.*
That way you'll make your writing better.

A *full stop* always marks the end.
It closes every sentence penned.

The *comma* is for small, short breaks,
And for lists the writer makes.

Dashes – like these – tell you something by
the way;
They give extra information (so do *brackets,*
I may say).

Full stops finish off: *colons* pause to
compare.
They also do this: list, explain and prepare.

The *semi-colon* makes a break; then comes
another clause.
It does the job of words that link – it's a
medium-length pause.

An *apostrophe* shows the owner of anyone's
things,
And it's also handy for shortenings.

I'm so glad! He's so mad! She's having
such a lark!
To show strong feeling you should use the
exclamation mark!

A *question mark* comes after What? When?
Where? and why? and how?
Do you? Could I? Shall we? Why not? Give
your answer, now!

"*Quotation marks*" enclose what's said.
Sometimes they're called "*speech marks*"
instead.

The capital letter and the full stop

Start sentences with a *capital letter*.
That way you'll make your writing better.

A *full stop* always marks the end.
It closes every sentence penned.

Always use a capital letter at the start of a sentence. Always end the sentence with a full stop.
You can tell a sentence because it has a subject and a verb, and needs no more words to make sense.
Punctuate the following. Find the subject and the verb. The first one is done for you.

the dog bit the postman yesterday

The dog bit the postman yesterday.

she went to school on her bike

....

it was a beautiful day for a picnic

....

time is getting on

....

the sea was really rough

....

go and get some potatoes from the shop

....

we hope you can come to the party

....

2

The comma

The *comma* is for small, short breaks,
And for lists the writer makes.

Commas are used to replace the very short
pauses for breath that you take naturally
at certain points when you say something.
Try these. The first one is done for you.

Mehmet hated swimming but he dived in.

Mehmet hated swimming, but he dived in.

The dog hearing them leave started to howl.

....

Leaping the fence the horse came towards
him.

....

I'd buy the red one I think if I were you.

....

Commas are also used to separate words in a
list, unless the word "and" does this already.
Try these. The first one is done for you.

He bought eggs butter cheese and yogurt.

He bought eggs, butter, cheese and yogurt.

She sprinted down the long dark narrow lane.

....

Everyone was running jumping and shouting
in the playground.

....

....

Dashes and brackets

Dashes – like these – tell you something by
the way;
They give extra information (so do *brackets*,
I may say).

Dashes and brackets mark an interruption in
the flow of a sentence to separate extra
information. Use dashes in less formal
places in your writing. Brackets always come
in pairs but you can use a single dash
before a new thought at the end of a sentence.

I am waiting and I will go on waiting until he
tells me.

I am waiting – and I will go on waiting –
until he tells me.

Katy, or Katie I am not sure how to spell her
name must be nearly two years old.

She lives at number six at least I think
that's where she lives.

The rest of the food if there is any left can
be eaten tomorrow.

We must leave now if we're really going.

4

The colon

Full stops finish off: *colons* pause to
                      compare.
They also do this: list, explain and prepare.

Sometimes a colon divides a sentence and
shows a contrast between the halves.
Usually, though, the colon introduces lists
of things, or is used instead of ''because'',
before giving an explanation.

He looked very smart he was wearing a suit.

He looked very smart: he was wearing a suit.

We went through many towns on the way
Marlborough, Swindon and Newbury.

....

....

Paul cannot go out today he has a bad cold.

....

You take that one I'll take the other.

....

Her dress was like a rainbow blue, green, red,
yellow and purple.

....

....

We urgently need more supplies paint,
brushes, wood, tools and cement.

....

....

The semi-colon

The *semi-colon* makes a break; then comes
another clause.
It does the job of words that link – it's a
medium-length pause.

Use a semi-colon instead of "and" or
"but". It makes a pause which is not as
strong as a full stop and so it joins the
ideas together.

We continued to search it was almost too
dark to see.

We continued to search; it was

almost too dark to see.

The man had come in he was leaning against
the fireplace.

....

....

They had disappeared we looked everywhere.

....

Come round early we could go out later.

....

I think we shall postpone the trip we might
go next year instead.

....

....

They ran faster they just caught the bus.

....

6

The apostrophe 1

An *apostrophe* shows the owner of anyone's
things,
And it's also handy for shortenings.

The apostrophe is used in two ways. First,
to show possession add an apostrophe plus an
s to the end of a word. If the word already
has an *s* on the end you may add only an
apostrophe. Make the following possessive.
The first one is done for you.

the lead of my dog .... *my dog's lead* ....

the hats of the men ....

the sides of the boats ....

the bike of James ....

the house of Mrs Charles ....

Some words showing possession *never* take an
apostrophe. These are: its, hers, his, ours,
yours, theirs. Write a sentence for each.

its ....

hers ....

his ....

ours ....

yours ....

theirs ....

7

The apostrophe 2

An *apostrophe* shows the owner of anyone's
things,
And it's also handy for shortenings.

The second way the apostrophe is used is
when two words are run together. It shows
that letters have been missed out. Always be
sure of which way you are using the
apostrophe.

I will → I'll   did not → didn't

She is not going to the fair.

She isn't going to the fair.

Mark cannot go because he has a cold.

....

We did not know what to do.

....

It was too high and he could not reach it.

....

Remember: you must *only* use an apostrophe
in "it's" *when you mean "it is"*, to show that
a letter has been missed out. Try these.

Its time we gave the dog its dinner.

....

Its a shame that its so late or we could
have seen its feeding time.

....

....

The question mark and the exclamation mark

I'm so glad! He's so mad! She's having such
a lark!
To show strong feeling you should use the
exclamation mark!

A question mark comes after What? When?
Where? and why? and how?
Do you? Could I? Shall we? Why not? Give
your answer, now!

After anything that asks a question put a
question mark. After an expression that
shows strong feeling put an exclamation
mark. The next word always starts with a
capital letter.

Are you going which way will you go

Are you going? Which way will you go?

I'm so tired how long before the end

....

What do you think I only wish I knew

....

Help it's freezing where is my jumper

....

Good heavens do you know what time it
is I had no idea it was so late

....

....

Hurry up do you think we've got all day

....

Quotation marks

"*Quotation marks*" enclose what's said.
Sometimes they're called "*speech marks*"
instead.

Only put quotation marks around any words
that have been spoken.
Punctuate the following sentences using
speech marks. Other kinds of punctuation
are given.
The first one is done for you.

Take care on these pavements, said Dad,
because they are very icy.

"Take care on these pavements," said Dad,
"because they are very icy."

I don't like it! shouted Sarah.

He has taken my lolly! sobbed the little boy.

Robert said Thank you.

Well, I don't know, said Bill, perhaps we
ought to find out.

Why don't you look in the dictionary? asked
her sister. It would probably explain the
word.

Punctuation practice

Practise these rules, don't hesitate;
Use all these marks to punctuate!

On the lines below write the following
passage using all the punctuation marks
you have learnt.

good morning said the postman theres a
parcel for you what is it said Billy excitedly
look cried Jane the postmark says America I
cut the string ripped off its brown paper and
lifted the lid off the box inside was something
shaped like an egg I couldnt tell what it was its
an American football stupid shouted Billy we
decided to take it outside and play with it
straight away it was the best present well not
quite the best I had ever received

....

....

....

....

....

....

....

....

....